Board Games
of the
50's, 60's & 70's

Layout and Design by
Stephanie Lane

Photography by
David Dilley

© **1994**

Published By

L-W BOOK SALES

P.O. Box 69
Gas City, IN 46933

Printed by IMAGE GRAPHICS, INC., Paducah, Kentucky

INTRODUCTION

Aha! What luck! Mom and Dad have brought home a new game! Children surround the commotion as it slowly emerges from within the package. Everyone's attention is gripped as they spy brilliant, cheery colors and the astonishing guarantee of "endless hours of non-stop fun." Impatiently surrounding the kitchen table, the entire family eagerly awaits to compete friend against friend, brother against sister, or anyone willing to test their skills. The box opens to reveal a selection of dice, instructions, and tiny trinkets: necessary tools to complete a fun-filled experience. Finally, as the board itself unfolds, imaginations unfold as well as the contestants scoot up to the table and prepare for an exciting evening . . . .

Games have always been an integral part of leisure time for both young and old alike. Since people have learned to communicate, they have developed all sorts of puzzles, games of chance, and competitions to test the wits of their friends and themselves. Every ancient culture has made a contribution, as archaeologists have discovered gaming boards and brain-teasers that have outlived the mighty empires that invented them.

Today our attention is focused on the "Baby Boomer Era of Board Games" – when the popularity of these games reached their peak. Creative and colorful, games were enjoyed by everyone for an after work diversion or when it was too dark to play outside. Game manufacturers recognized this opportunity to present games of all sorts, reflecting the various interests and vast differences of the eager game-playing public throughout the nation.

These game companies suggested above thrived during this period. Hundreds of companies designed games to compete for shelf space in this market, while a few major companies were established enough to become household names as popular as the games they offered. Parker Brothers, Milton Bradley, Hasbro and others managed to cover the shelves of large retail outlets and smaller shops alike with colorful packages boasting endless amounts of fun.

While games of all sorts appeared, an obviously profound influence at the time of the "Baby Boomer Era of Board Games" was TELEVISION. Not only would you witness the lively advertisements on the TV, many games themselves were patterned after choice programs. Countless boxed games were fashioned after cartoon characters, action/adventure heroes and heroines, current popular quiz shows, the eerie atmosphere surrounding the current mystery/spy genre and the science fiction/horror craze of the time. Television also prompted still more interest in world events and exotic locales, giving rise to board games depicting infamous military conflicts and enlightening games from foreign cultures.

With an elaborate history behind it, the subject of board games was destined to become a major collectible. Nearly every yard sale and flea market will reveal a chance to grasp a low-priced specimen, while the rarer and more popular games can be discovered at antique and toy shows everywhere, yet the prices may be less favorable to the eager collector. These prices shall no longer remain as much of a mystery. For that reason this price guide was constructed. Now the <u>real</u> fun game begins: to discover these finds and add them to your own!

PRICING NOTE

The current prices in this book should be used only as a guide. They are not to set prices, which vary from one section of the country to another. Dealers prices vary greatly and are affected by condition as well as demand. The prices established in this guide are for games that are in fine condition. Lesser condition will bring much lower prices and mint condition will bring higher!!! The publisher assumes no responsibility for any losses or gains that might be incurred as a result of consulting this guide.

The $10,000 Pyramid, 1974,
by Milton Bradley Company.
$10

The $20,000 Pyramid, 1977,
by Milton Bradley Company.
$10

10-Four, Good Buddy, 1976,
by Parker Brothers.
$15

12 o'clock High Game,
1965, by Ideal.
$50

77 Sunset Strip, 1960,
by Lowell.
$60

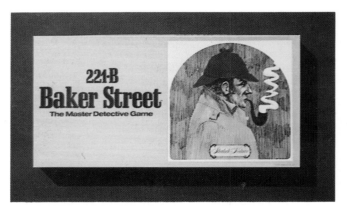

221-B Baker Street, 1977,
by Hansen.
$20

Acquire, 1976,
by Avalon Hill.
$15

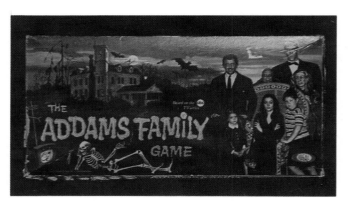

The Addams Family Game, 1964,
by Ideal.
$100

Adventures of Lassie, 1955,
by Lisbeth Whiting.
$35

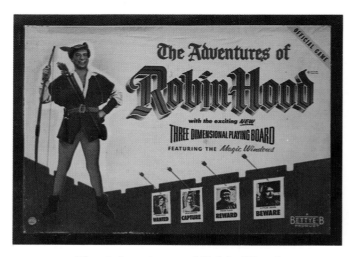

The Adventures of Robin Hood,
1956, by Bettye-B.
$75

Aggravation, deluxe party edition,
1972, by Lakeside.
$10

Alfred Hitchcock Why Mystery Game,
1958, by Milton Bradley.
$25

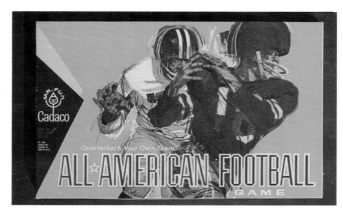

All-American Football Game,
1965, by Cadaco.
$25

The All in the Family Game,
1972, by Milton Bradley.
$20

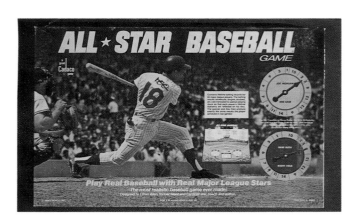

All ☆ Star Baseball Game,
1968, by Cadaco.
$25

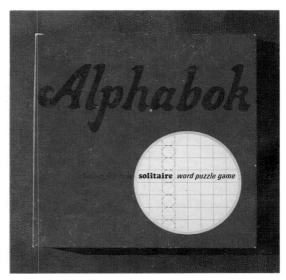

Alphabok, 1968,
by Springbok.
$20

The Amazing Spider Man Game with
The Fantastic Four!.
1977, by Milton Bradley
$65

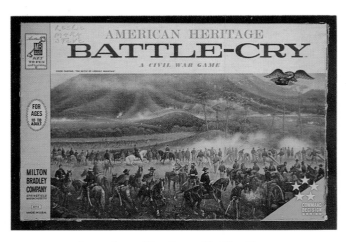

American Heritage Battle-Cry,
A Civil War Game, 1961,
by Milton Bradley.
$40

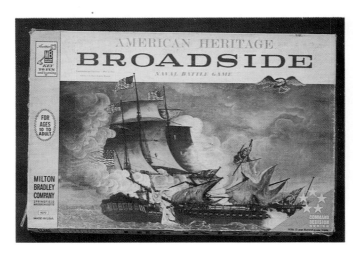

American Heritage Broadside, Naval Battle Game,
1962, by Milton Bradley.
$40

American Heritage Dogfight, Air Battle Game,
World War I, 1962, by Milton Bradley.
$40

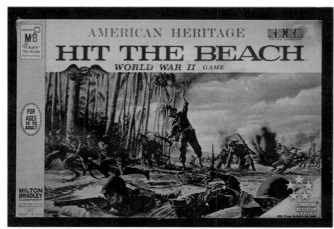

American Heritage Hit The Beach,
World War II Game, 1965, by Milton Bradley.
$35

American Heritage Skirmish, A Revolutionary
War Game, 1975, by Milton Bradley.
$30

Animal Fun, 1968,
by Milton Bradley.
$15

Annie Oakley Game, 1950's,
by Milton Bradley.
$50

The Archie Game, 1969,
by Whitman-West. Publ.
$35

Around the World in 80 Days, 1957,
by Transogram.
$40

Art Linkletter's House Party Game,
1968, by Whitman.
$30

Astro Launch, 1963,
by Ohio Art.
$80

Autobridge, 1959,
by Autobridge Company.
$15

Avanté, 1967,
by Fyanes Corporation.
$10

Board Games Not Pictured

2 For The Money
1955, by Hasbro $35

20,000 Leagues Under The Sea
1975, by Lakeside $20

101 Dalmations
1960, by Whitman $30

300 Mile Race
1955, by Warren $55

1863
1961, by Parker Brothers $40

4000 AD
1972, by Waddington $30

Abbott & Costello, "Who's On First?
1978, by Selchow and Righter . . . $20

Acme Checkout Game
1959, by Milton Bradley $35

Acorn Hunt, Alvin, Theodore & Simon
1960, by Hasbro $40

Across The Board Horse Racing Game
1975, by MPH Company $15

Action Baseball
1967, by Pressman $50

Ad-Dic-Tion
1968, by Cre-Tek $15

Ad-Lib
1970, by E.S. Lowe $15

Addams Family Game
1973, by Milton Bradley $35

Adventures of Davy Crockett
1950's $55

Adventures of Popeye
1957, by Transogram $85

Air Empire
1961, by Avalon Hill $85

Air Race Around The World
1950, by Lido Toy Company $30

Air Traffic Controller
1974, by Schaper $30

Airline, The Jet Age Game
1977, by MPH $25

Airport
1972, by Dynamic Games $20

Airways
1950, by Lindstorm Tool
   & Toy Co. $40

Alien
1979, by Kenner $40

All Time Greats Baseball
1971, by Midwest Research $15

All-Pro Basketball
1969, by Ideal $20

All-Pro Football
1967, by Ideal $20

All-Star Football
1950's, by Gardner & Co $15

Allen Sherman's Camp Grenada
1965, by Milton Bradley $35

Alumni Fun
1964, by Milton Bradley $30

**Alvin and the Chipmunks
Big Record Game**
1960, by Hasbro $60

**Amazing Spider-Man Web
Spinning Action Game**
1979, by Ideal $40

American Airlines Travel Game
1955, by Milton Bradley $35

American Derby
1951, by Cadaco-Ellis $40

Animal Talk
1963, by Mattel $50

Annette's Secret Passage
1960, by Parker Brothers $40

Apollo, Voyage to the Moon
1969, by Tracianne $35

Approved Little League Baseball
1950's, by Toycraft $60

Aquanauts
1960, by Transogram $40

Aquarius 2000
1970, by Gamescience $35

Archie's Fun Game
1963, by Hasbro $45

Arnold Palmer's Inside Golf
1961, by D.B. Remson $50

Arrest and Trial
1963, by Transogram $40

**Art Linkletter's Game of
"People Are Funny"**
1954, by Whitman $30

As The World Turns
1966, by Parker Brothers $40

ASG Major League Baseball
1973, Gerney Games $40

Assembly Line
1953, by Selchow & Righter . . . $50

Astron
1955, by Parker Brothers $60

Atom Ant Saves the Day
1966, By Transogram $100

Ax Your Tax
1979, by Barbara
   Doyle-Carlton $25

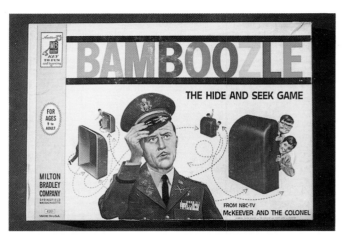

Bamboozle, 1962,
by Milton Bradley.
$20

Barbie's Keys to Fame,
1963, by Mattel.
$50

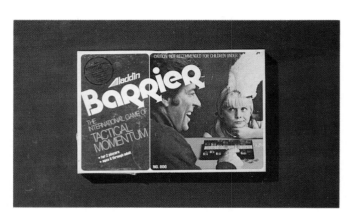

Barrier, 1974,
by Aladdin.
$20

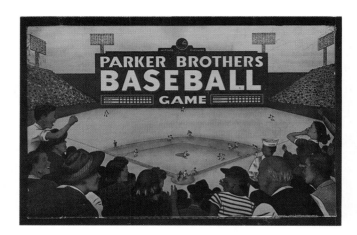

Baseball Game, 1950,
by Parker Brothers.
$35

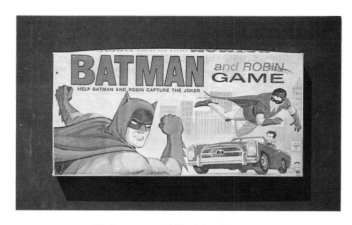

Batman and Robin Game,
1965, by Hasbro.
$100

Batman Game, 1966,
by Milton Bradley.
$60

The Battle of Britain, History restaged!,
1968, by Game Science.
$20

The Battle of the Bulge, 1965,
by Avalon Hill.
$40

Battleship, 1978,
by Milton Bradley.
$15

Battlestar Galactica,1978,
by Parker Brothers.
$20

"Battle Stations!", 1952,
by John E. Burleson.
$50

Beat Detroit, 1972,
by Dynamic Games.
$20

Beat The Clock, 1954,
by Lowell Toy Corporation.
$60

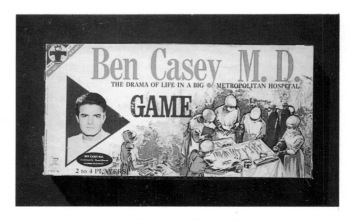

Ben Casey MD, 1961,
by Transogram.
$35

Big Business, 1958,
by Transogram.
$20

Big Foot, 1977,
by Milton Bradley.
$20

Bingo, 1950's,
by Pressman.
$20

The Bionic Woman, 1976,
by Parker Brothers.
$20

Black Hole Space Alert Game,
Escape The Doomed Cygnus, 1979,
by Whitman-Western Publication.
$20

The Game of Blast, 1973,
by Ideal.
$20

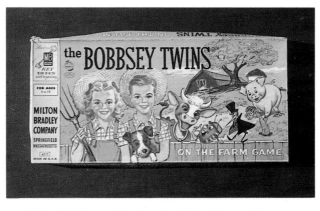

The Bobbsey Twins On The Farm Game,
1957, by Milton Bradley.
$40

Body English, 1967,
by Milton Bradley.
$20

Bonanza Michigan Rummy,
1964, Parker Brothers.
$35

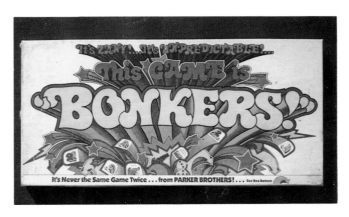

This Game Is Bonkers,
1978, by Parker Brothers.
$10

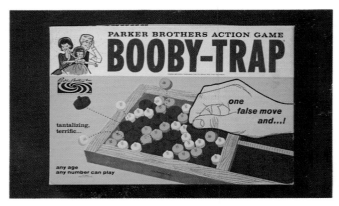

Booby-Trap, 1965,
by Parker Brothers.
$10

Break The Bank, 1977,
Milton Bradley.
$10

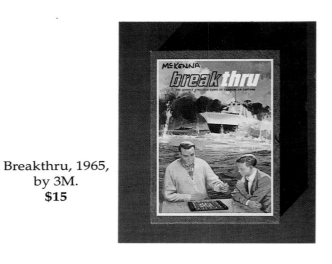

Breakthru, 1965,
by 3M.
$15

The Bride Game,
1971,
by Selchow and
Righter.
$30

The Buccaneers, 1957,
by Transogram.
$40

"Buck Rogers" Game, 1979,
by Milton Bradley.
$30

Bamm Bamm, Color Me Happy
1963, by Transogram $85

Banana Splits
1969, by Hasbro $35

Bang, A Game of the Old West
1950's, by Selchow & Righter . . . $50

Bantu
1955, by Parker Brothers $35

Barbie Queen of the Prom
1960, by Mattel $35

Baretta
1976, by Milton Bradley $20

Barnabas Collins
Dark Shadows Game
1969, by Milton Bradley $80

Barney Miller
1977, by Parker Brothers $15

Baseball Strategy
1973, by Avalon Hill $15

Bash
1965, by Milton Bradley $20

Bat Masterson
1958, by Lowell $85

Battle Line Game
1964, by Ideal $55

Battle of Atlanta
1960, by Southern Games $65

Battle of the Planets
1979, by Milton Bradley $35

Battleboard
1972, by Ideal $30

Beachhead Invasion Game
1950's, by Warren
   "Built-Rite" $35

Beany & Cecil Match It Game
1961, by Mattel $30

Beatle "Flip Your Wig"
1964, by Milton Bradley $125

Beetle Bailey
1956, by Jaymar $65

Behind the 8 Ball
1969, by Selchow & Righter $30

Benji
1976, by House of Games $15

Bermuda Triangle
1975, by Milton Bradley $20

Beverly Hillbillies
1963, by Toycraft $75

Bewitch
1964, Selchow & Righter $25

Bewitched
1965, by Game Gems $65

Bicentennial Games
1975, by Coach House $15

Big Game
1950, by National Games $50

Big League Baseball
1966, by 3M $35

Big Sneeze
1968, by Ideal $20

Big Time Operator
1956, by Bettye-B $40

Big Town
1954, by Lowell $65

Big Wig
1973, by Explorations $35

Billionaire
1956, by Happy Hour Inc $25

Bing Crosby Call Me Lucky
1954, by Parker Brothers $65

Bionic Crisis
1976, by Parker Brothers $20

Bird Watcher
1956, by Parker Brothers $75

Black Beauty
1957, by Transogram $30

Blast Off!
1953, by Selchow & Righter $75

Blizzard of '77
1977, by C.P. Marino $15

Blondie & Dagwood Race for the Office
1950, by Jaymar $75

Blue Line Hockey
1968, by 3M $40

Bob Feller's Big League Baseball
1950's, by Saalfield $125

Book of Lists Game
1979, by Avalon Hill $15

Boom or Bust
1951, by Parker Brothers $100

Boomers, Fighters & Bombers
1970's, by Schmid $10

Boondoggle, The Game of Comic Elections
1952, by Selchow & Righter $55

Boris Karloff Monster Game
1965, by Game Gems $125

Bottle Hunt
1974, by Camcar $20

Bowl and Score
1974, by E.S. Lowe $20

Bowl Bound
1978, by Avalon Hill -
Sports Illustrated $10

Brainstorm
1972, by Lowe $15

Branded
1965, by Milton Bradley $75

Break The Bank
1955, by Bettye-B $60

Bruce Force "Lost in Outer Space"
1963, by Ideal $85

Buck Rogers
1965, by Transogram $85

Buckaroo
1950's, by Milton Bradley $30

Buffalo Bill Jr.'s Cattle Round Up
1956, by Built-Rite $45

Bugs Bunny Adventure Game
1961, by Milton Bradley $65

Bullwinkle Travel Adventure Game
1970, by Transogram $75

Bullwinkle's Hide 'N Seek
1961, by Milton Bradley $75

Burke's Law
1963, by Transogram $30

Buttons & Bows
1960, by Transogram $40

Camelot, 1955,
by Parker Brothers.
$35

Camouflage, 1961,
by Milton Bradley.
$40

Captain America Game, 1966,
by Milton Bradley.
$65

Captain Video, 1952,
by Milton Bradley.
$100

Careers, 1958,
by Parker Brothers.
$20

Carrier Strike!, 1977,
by Milton Bradley.
$30

17

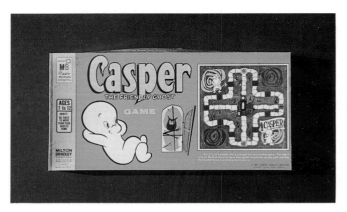

Casper The Friendly Ghost Game,
1959, Milton Bradley.
$50

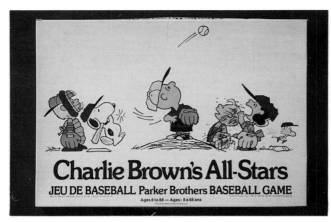

Charlie Brown's All-Stars Baseball Game,
1965, by Parker Brothers.
$40

Charlie's Angels Game, 1977,
by Milton Bradley.
$15

Cheyenne Game, Shooting Rifle,
1958, by Milton Bradley.
$60

Chinese Checkers, 1971,
by Hasbro.
$10

Chit Chat, The Hugh Downs Game of Conversation,
1963, by Milton Bradley.
$25

Chitty•Chitty•Bang•Bang Game,
1968, by Milton Bradley.
$20

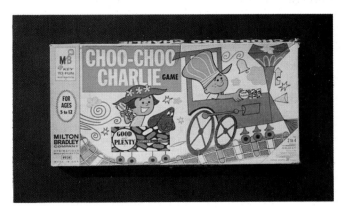

Choo-Choo Charlie Game,
1968, by Milton Bradley.
$20

Close Encounters of the Third Kind,
1978, by Parker Brothers.
$20

"Clue", 1956,
by Parker Brothers.
$15

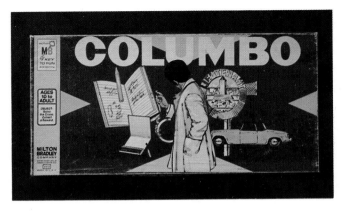

Columbo Detective Game,
1973, by Milton Bradley.
$15

Combat!,
1963, by Ideal.
$50

Concentration,
1955, by Milton Bradley.
$30

Cootie, 1950's,
by W.H. Schaper Mfg.,
Company, Inc.
$20

Corner The Market, Buy and Sell,
1953, by Whitman.
$20

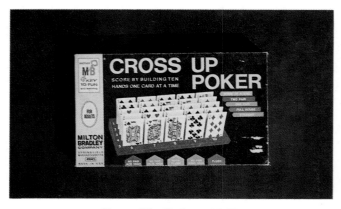

Cross Up Poker, 1968,
by Milton Bradley.
$15

Cross Up, The Competitive Crossword Game,
1974, by Milton Bradley.
$15

Call It Golf
1966, by A. Strauss $20

Call My Bluff
1965, by Milton Bradley $30

Camp Runamuck
1965, by Ideal $30

Campaign! The American Go Game
1961, by Saalfield $85

Candid Camera Game
1963, by Lowell $50

Canoga
1972, by Pacific Game Co $15

Caper: The Jewel Robbery
1970, by Parker Brothers $20

Capital Air Race
1955, by Capital Airlines $50

**Captain Gallant of the
Foreign Legion**
1955, by Transogram $75

Captain Kangaroo
1956, by Milton Bradley $30

Car 54 Where Are You
1961, by Allison Toys $100

Careful: The Toppling Tower Game
1967, by Ideal $10

Cars 'N Trucks Build-a-Game
1961, by Ideal $85

Case of the Elusive Assassin
1967, by Ideal $50

Casey Jones Game Box
1959, by Saalfield $35

Casey Jones Jr. Railroad Game
1959, by Saalfield $35

Cat & Mouse Game
1964, by Parker Brothers $25

Catchword
1954, by Whitman $15

Challenge The Yankees
1964, by Hasbro $175

Charge It!
1972, by Whitman $15

Cherry Ames Nursing Game
1959, by Parker Brothers $55

Chevyland Sweepstakes
1968, by Milton Bradley $50

Cheyenne (with Pistol)
1958, by Milton Bradley $60

Chop Suey Game
1966, by Ideal $20

Chopper Strike
1976, by Milton Bradley $20

Chubby Checker Limbo Game
1961, by Wham-o $75

Chubby Checker Twister
1960's, by Empire $75

Chutes Away Air Rescue Game
1970's, by Gabriel $30

Chutzpah
1967, by Cadaco $30

Cimarron Strip
1966, by Ideal $60

Civil War Game
1961, by Parker Brothers $40

Class Struggle
1978, Ollman $20

Code Name: Sector
1977, by Parker Brothers $15

Cold Feet
1967, by Ideal $20

College Basketball
1954, by Cadaco-Ellis $20

Combat!
1965, by Milton Bradley $35

Compatibility
1974, by Reiss $10

Conflict
1960, by Parker Brothers $35

Conquest
1972, by Benge $15

Contigo
1972, by 3M $15

Cooks Tours-European Travel Game
1972, by Selchow & Righter $25

Countdown to Space
1960, by Transogram $40

Countdown: Adventure In Space
1967, by E. S. Lowe $45

Counter Ploy
1975, by Hanlon-Red Raparee . . $20

Counter Point
1976, by Hallmark $10

Coup D'Etat
1966, Parker Brothers $30

Cowboy Roundup
1952, by Parker Brothers $30

Cracker Jack Game
1976, by Milton Bradley $20

Crazy Clock
1964, by Ideal $40

Creature Castle
1975, by Whitman $35

Creature From the Black Lagoon
1963, by Hasbro $175

Crosswords
1953, by Jaymar $20

Dastardly and Muttley in their Flying Machines,
1969, by Milton Bradley.
$55

The Dating Game,
1967, by Hasbro.
$30

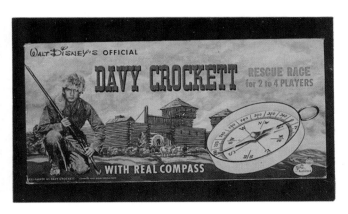

Davy Crockett Rescue Race,
1955, by Gabriel.
$60

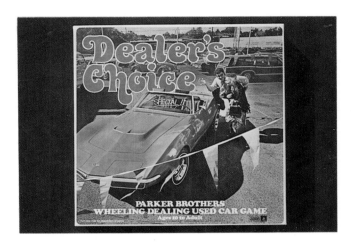

Dealer's Choice, 1972,
by Parker Brothers.
$20

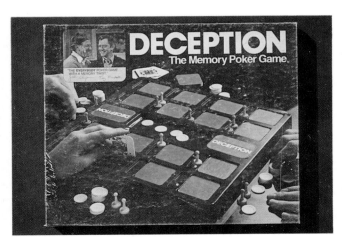

Deception, The Memory Poker Game,
1975, by Milton Bradley.
$10

Deduction, 1976,
by Ideal.
$10

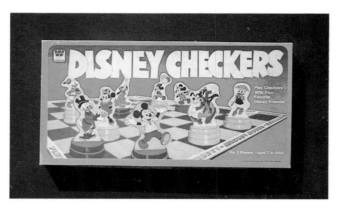

Disney Checkers, 1977
by Whitman.
$20

Disneyland Monorail Game,
1960, by Parker Brothers.
$30

Doctor, Doctor! Game,
1978, by Ideal.
$15

Dollar A Second, 1955,
by Lowell Toy Corporation.
$50

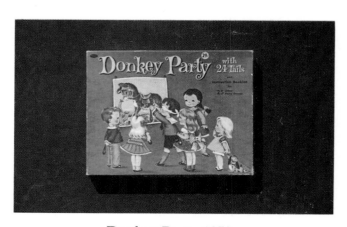

Donkey Party, 1952,
by Whitman.
$15

Double Cross, 1974,
by Lakeside Games.
$15

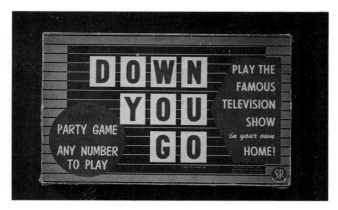

Down You Go, 1954,
by Selchow and Righter Company.
$20

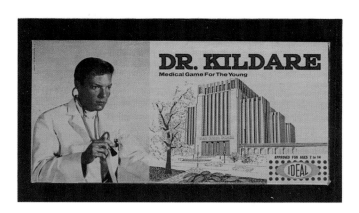

Dr. Kildare, 1962,
by Ideal.
$40

Drip Dragster, 1971,
by Colorforms.
$20

Dumy Rumy, 1969,
by Family Game Specialists.
$10

Dungeon Dice, 1977,
by Parker Brothers.
$15

Dungeons & Dragons,
Basic Set,
1978, by TSR.
$20

Dan Kersteter's Classic Football
1971, by Big League Game Co... $20

Dark Shadows
1968, by Whitman $80

Davy Crockett Frontierland Game
1955, by Parker Brothers $75

Davy Crockett Radar Action Game
1955, by Ewing $90

Decathlon
1972, by Sports Illustrated $15

Decoy
1956, by Selchow & Righter $40

Democracy
1969, by Western Publishing . . . $25

Dennis The Menace Game
1960, by Standard Toykraft $85

Dennis The Menace Tiddley Winks
1961, by Whitman $20

Deputy Dawg
1960, by Milton Bradley $45

Derby Day
1959, by Parker Brothers $75

Detectives
1961, by Transogram $40

Dick Tracy A Sunday Funnies
1972, by Ideal $85

Dick Tracy Crime Stopper
1963, by Ideal $150

Dick Tracy
1961, by Selchow & Righter $75

Dick Van Dyke
1965, by Toykraft $60

Diner's Club Game
1961, by Ideal $75

Dino the Dinosaur
1962, by Transogram $35

Diplomacy
1961, by Avalon Hill $40

Discovery Home Game
1955, by Lowell $20

Disney Mousketeer
1964, by Parker Brothers $75

Disneyland Game
1965, by Whitman $30

Dispatcher
1958, by Avalon Hill $100

Diver Dan
1961, by Milton Bradley $30

Doc Holiday Wild West
1960, by Transogram $45

Doctor Who
1975, by Denys Fisher $85

Dog Race
1955, by Transogram $45

Dogfight
1962, by Milton Bradley $30

Dondi Finders Keepers
1959, by Hasbro $60

Dondi Potato Race
1960, by Hasbro $60

Donny and Marie Osmond
1976, by Mattel $25

Dracula Mystery Game
1963, by Hasbro $150

Dragnet
1955, by Transogram $75

Dragnet-Badge 714 Radar Action
1955, by Knickerbocker Plastic . . $75

Dream Date
1963, by Transogram $50

Dream House TV Home Game
1968, by Milton Bradley $25

Driver Training Games
1959, by Decor Note $25

Driver-Ed
1969, by Visual Dynamics $20

Dualing
1977, by Elder Industries $20

Dudley Do-Right's Find Snidely
1976, by Whitman $25

Dune
1979, by Avalon Hill $30

Dynamite Shack
1968, Milton Bradley $20

The Game of Easy Money,
1974, by Milton Bradley.
$20

Egg-citement!, 1973,
by Cadaco.
$20

Elvis Welcomes You To His World,
1978, by Duff Sisters, Inc.
$35

The Emergency! Game,
1973, by Milton Bradley.
$20

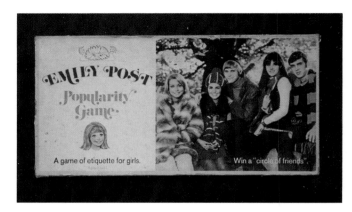

Emily Post Popularity Game,
1970, by Selchow and Righter.
$40

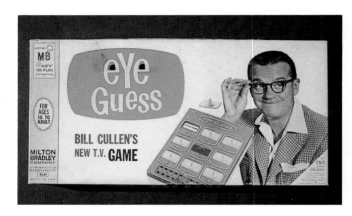

Eye Guess, Bill Cullen's New TV Game,
1966, by Milton Bradley.
$40

Ecology
1970, by Urban Systems $15

Election 68
1967, by Createk $30

Elliot Ness & The Untouchables
1961, by Transogram $75

Ellsworth Elephant Game
1960, by Selchow & Righter $45

Elvis Presley, King of Rock Game
1978, by Lee/Raymond $35

Emergency
1973, by Parker Brothers $20

Enemy Agent
1976, by Milton Bradley $25

Energy Crisis
1973, Itemation $15

Engineer
1957, Selchow & Righter $20

Ensign O'Toole: USS Appleby
1963, by Hasbro $40

Ergo
1977, by Invecta Games $10

Escape From Colditz
1960, by Parker Brothers $60

Escape from the Casbah
1975, by Selchow & Righter $20

Everybody's Talking
1967, by Watkins Strathmore . . . $20

Extra Innings
1975, by J. Kavanaugh $15

The F.B.I. Game, 1961,
by Transogram.
$60

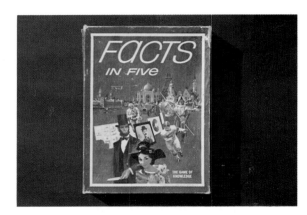

Facts In Five, 1976,
by Avalon Hill Game Company.
$20

The Family Affair Game, "Where's Mrs. Beasley?"
1971, by Whitman.
$30

"Family Feud", 2nd Edition,
1978, by Milton Bradley.
$10

Fangface, 1979,
by Parker Brothers.
$40

The Farming Game, 1979,
by Weekend Farmer.
$40

Fascination, the electric maze game,
1961, by Remco.
$15

The Original Game of Fascination Checkers,
1962, by Remco.
$15

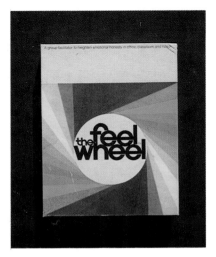

The Feel Wheel, 1972,
by Dynamic Games.
$15

Felix The Cat Game, 1960,
by Milton Bradley.
$65

Finance, 1958,
by Parker Brothers.
$30

Flash Gordon, Adventures on the Moons of
Mongo Game, 1977,
by House of Games, Waddingtons.
$40

The Flintstones Game, 1971,
by Milton Bradley.
$40

The Fonz Hanging Out At Arnold's,
1976, by Milton Bradley.
$30

Frantic Frogs Action Wind-up Game,
1965, by Milton Bradley.
$75

F Troop
1965, by Ideal $85

Face the Facts
1961, by Lowell $30

Fall, Wrestling Game
1950's, by National $65

Family Affair
1968, by Remco $50

Family Game
1967, by Hasbro $30

Fantastic Voyage
1958, by Milton Bradley $25

Fantasy Island
1978, by Ideal $20

Fantasyland Game
1956, by Parker Brothers $30

Fast Golf
1977, by Whitman $15

FBI Crime Resistance Game
1976, by Milton Bradley $15

Feed The Elephant
1952, by Cadaco $25

Fess Parker Trail Blazers
1964, by Milton Bradley $55

Feudal
1967, by 3M $15

Fighter-Bomber
1977, by Cadaco $30

Fire Fighters!
1957, by Saalfield $35

Fireball XL5
1964, by Milton Bradley $75

Fish Bait Game
1965, by Ideal $40

Flash Gordon
1965, by Game Gems $40

Flash, The Press Photographer Game
1956, by Selchow & Righter $75

Flea Circus
1964, by Mattel $20

Flight Captain
1972, by E.S. Lowe $25

Flintstone's Hoppy the Hopparoo
1966, by Transogram $75

Flintston's Big Game Hunt
1962, by Whitman $80

Flintstones Breakball
1962, by Whitman $70

Flintstones Stone Age Game
1961, by Transogram $70

Flip Flop Go
1962, by Mattel $20

Flipper Flips
1965, by Mattel $20

Flying Nun
1968, by Milton Bradley $35

Foil
1968, by 3M $25

Formula-1
1963, by Parker Brothers $40

Fortune Telling
1969, by All Fair $15

Forty Niners
1950, by National Games $50

Frankenstein Game
1963, by Hasbro $150

Frontier Fort Rescue Race
1956, by Gabriel $35

Fu Manchu's Hidden Hoard
1967, by Ideal $45

Fugitive
1966, by Ideal $130

Fun on the Farm
1957, by Milton Bradley $20

Funny Bones
1968, by Parker Brothers $20

Fury Game
1956, by Mousely $15

Gambler, 1977,
by Parker Brothers.
$20

Game of India, 1950's
by Whitman.
$25

Game of State Capitals, 1952,
by Parker Brothers.
$30

Game of the States, 1960,
by Milton Bradley.
$20

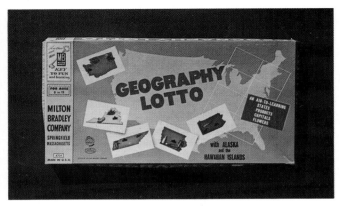

Geography Lotto, 1956,
by Milton Bradley.
$25

Gettysburg Battle Game, 1977,
by Avalon Hill.
$30

Giant Backgammon Rug Set,
1974, by Itemation.
$15

Godzilla Game, 1978,
by Mattel.
$60

Goldilocks, 1954,
by Cadaco-Ellis.
$30

Gooses Wild, 1966,
by Co-5 Co., Inc.
$15

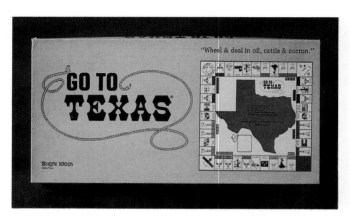

Go To Texas, 1979,
by Bright Ideas.
$20

Grab-A-Loop, 1968,
by Milton Bradley.
$30

To Grandmother's House We Go, 1974,
by Cadaco.
$20

Green Ghost Game, 1965,
by Transogram.
$75

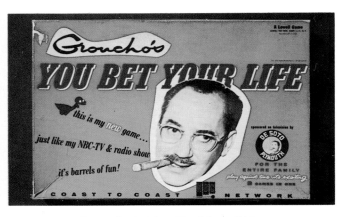

Groucho's You Bet Your Life,
1955, by Lowell.
$100

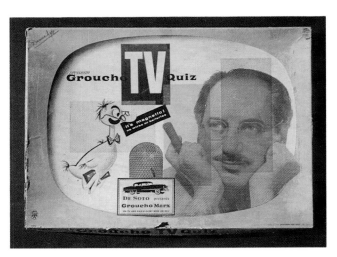

Groucho TV Quiz, 1954,
by Pressman.
$100

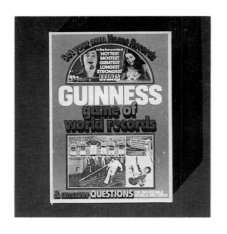

Guinness Game Of World Records and
Answer Questions, 1975, by Parker Brothers.
$10

Gung Ho, 1961,
by Lowe.
$15

G.I. Joe Combat Infantry Game
1964, by Hasbro $100

G.I. Joe Navy Frogman Game
1964, by Hasbro $100

Gambler's Golf
1975, by Gammon Games $15

Game of Black Beauty
1958, by Transogram $30

Game of Coney Island
1957, by Selchow & Righter $35

Game of Hollywood Stars
1955, by Whitman $30

Game of Scoop
1956, by Parker Brothers $45

Game of the Week
1969, by Hasbro $35

Game of Traps
1950's, by Trap's Mfg. $50

Game of Yertle
1960, by Revell $60

Games of Arabian Nights
1950, by National Games $40

Gang Way for Fun
1964, by Transogram $65

Garrison's Gorillas
1967, by Ideal $50

Garroway's Game of Possession
1955, by Remco $40

Gas Crisis
1979, by MacMillan $15

Gene Autry's Dude Ranch Game
1956, by Built-Rite $70

Geo-Graphy
1958, by Cadaco-Ellis $20

George of the Jungle
1968, by Parker Brothers $85

Get Smart Time Bomb Game
1965, by Ideal $70

Get That License
1955, by Selchow & Righter $35

Get The Message
1964, by Milton Bradley $20

Gidget Fortune Teller
1965, by Milton Bradley $35

Gidget Game
1965, by Standard Toycraft $30

Gilligan's Island
1965, by Game Gems $100

Global Air Race
1952, by Replogle Globes Inc. . . . $75

Go For The Green!
1973, by Sports Illustrated $15

Go For Broke
1965, by Selchow & Righter $25

Go to the Head of the Class
1955, by Milton Bradley $20

Godfather Game
1971, by Family Games $40

Godzilla Game
1963, by Ideal $110

Going To Jerusalem
1955, by Parker Brothers $45

Goldfinger
1966, by Milton Bradley $30

Gomer Pyle Game
1964, by Transogram $80

Gong Show
1977, by American Publishing . . . $25

Goofy Finds His Marbles
1970, by Whitman $35

Grand Slam
1979, by Sming Game Co. $30

Gray Ghost
1958, by Transogram $60

Grease
1978, by Milton Bradley $15

Great Escape Game
1967, by Ideal $35

Green Acres
1965, by Toykraft $55

Green Hornet Quick Switch Game
1966, by Milton Bradley $200

Grizzly Adams
1978, by Waddington $20

Guadalcanal
1966, by Avalon Hill $25

Gumby and Pokey Playful Trails
1968, by Co-5 Co. $50

Gunsmoke
1958, by Lowell $75

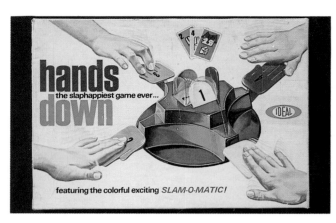

Hands Down, 1965,
by Ideal.
$20

Hangman, 1976,
by Milton Bradley.
$15

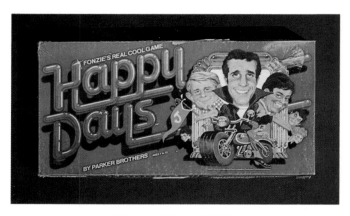

Happy Days, 1976,
by Parker Brothers.
$15

The Happy Little Train Game,
1957, by Milton Bradley.
$20

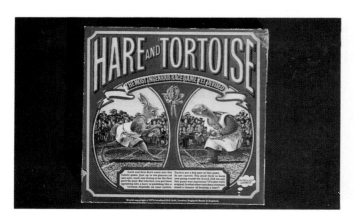

Hare and Tortoise, 1973,
by Intellect (U.K.).
$30

Hats Off, 1967,
by Kohner Brothers.
$30

Headache, 1977,
by Gabriel.
$20

Hi-Ho! Cherry-O,
1960, by Whitman.
$20

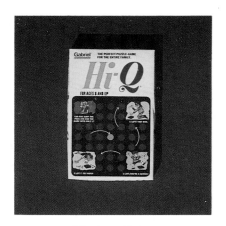

Hi-Q, 1975,
by Gabriel.
$20

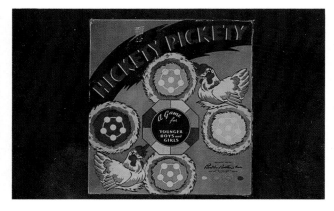

Hickety Pickety, 1954,
by Parker Brothers.
$25

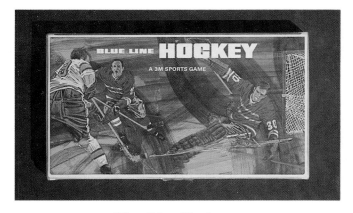

Blue Line Hockey,
1968, by 3M.
$40

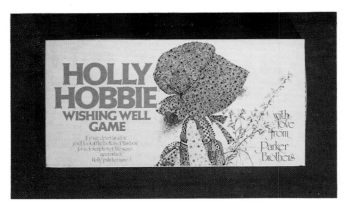

Holly Hobbie Wishing Well Game,
1976, by Parker Brothers.
$15

The Hollywood Squares TV Game,
1974, by Ideal.
$15

Horsin' Around, 1960's
by Play-Doh/Rainbow Crafts.
$30

Howdy Doody's Electric Carnival Game,
1950's, by Harett-Gilmar.
$100

Huckleberry Hound Western Game,
1959, by Milton Bradley.
$60

Hulla Baloo Electric Teen Game,
1965, by Remco.
$40

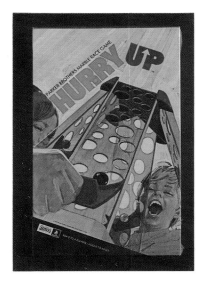

Hurry Up, 1971,
by Parker Brothers.
$20

Hūsker Dū,
1970, by Regina.
$20

Hang On Harvey!
1969, by Ideal $15

Hardy Boys Treasure Game
1957, by Parker Brothers $35

Harlem Globetrotters Game
1971, by Milton Bradley $40

Harpoon, The Real Whale Hunt Game
1955, by Gabriel & Sons $70

Hashimoto San
1960, by Transogram $50

Hat in the Ring
1971, by Kiphinger Washington
　Editions $25

Have Gun, Will Travel
1959, by Parker Brothers $80

Hawaii Five O
1968, by Remco $45

Hawaiian Eye
1963, by Lowell $75

Hawaiian Eye
1960, by Transogram $120

Hawaiian Punch
1977, by Mattel $30

Haunted House
1962, by Ideal $100

Hector Heathcote
1963, by Transogram $100

Hex: The Zig-Zag Game
1950, by Parker Brothers $20

Hide 'n Thief
1965, by Whitman $25

High Gear Game
1962, by Mattel $30

High Hand
1964, by Milton Bradley $15

High Spirits
1962, by Milton Bradley $35

Hit the Beach
1965, by Milton Bradley $45

Hobbit Game
1977, American Publishing $35

Hocus Pocus
1968, by Transogram $20

Hogan's Heroes
1966, by Transogram $65

Holiday
1958, by Replogle Globes Inc . . . $40

Home Team Baseball Game
1957, by Selchow & Righter $40

Honey West
1965, by Ideal $70

Hookey: Go Fishin'
1974, by Cadaco $15

Hoopla
1966, by Ideal $20

Hopalong Cassidy
1950, by Milton Bradley $85

Hot Wheels Wipe Out
1968, by Mattel $45

How To Succeed In Business
1963, by Milton Bradley $25

Howdy Doody's 3-Ring Circus
1950, by Harett-Gilmar $75

Howdy Doody's Own Game
1950's, by Parker Brothers $85

Howdy Doody's TV Game
1950's, by Milton Bradley $85

Huckleberry Hound & Yogi Bear Break-a-Plate
1961, by Transogram $60

Huckleberry Hound Bumps Game
1961, by Transogram $60

Huckleberry Hound Juggle Roll
1960, by Transogram $60

Huckleberry Hound Spin-O
1959, by Bardell $60

I Dream of Jeannie Game,
1965, by Milton Bradley.
$50

"I Spy" Game, 1965,
by Ideal.
$75

The Incredible Hulk Game with the
Fantastic Four, 1978, by Milton Bradley.
$30

The Inventors, 1974,
by Parker Brothers.
$25

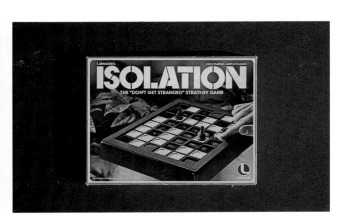

Isolation, 1978,
by Lakeside.
$15

I'm Garry Moore . . . and I've Got A Secret,
1956, by Lowell.
$40

Image
1972, by 3M $15

Intercept
1978, by Lakeside $20

Intrigue
1965, by Universal Games $15

Intrigue
1956, by Milton Bradley $35

Ipcress File
1966, by Milton Bradley $40

Ironside
1967, by Ideal $80

It Takes Two
1970, by Hasbro $25

It's About Time
1967, by Ideal $85

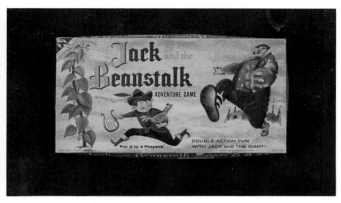

Jack and the Beanstalk Adventure Game,
1957, by Transogram.
$50

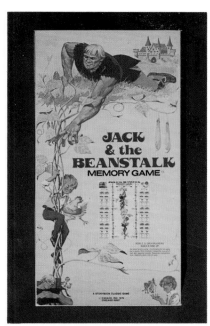

Jack and the
Beanstalk Memory
Game,
1976, by Cadaco.
$25

Jackie Gleason's "And Awa-a-a-a-y We Go!
TV Fun Game, 1956, by Transogram.
$125

Jame Bond 007 Game "Goldfinger",
1966, by Milton Bradley.
$60

James Bond 007 "Thunderball" Game,
1965, by Milton Bradley.
$60

James Bond Secret Agent 007 Game,
1964, by Milton Bradley.
$35

Jan Murray's Treasure Hunt,
1957, by Gardner Games.
$45

Jan Murray's Charge Account
TV Word Game, 1961, by Lowell.
$45

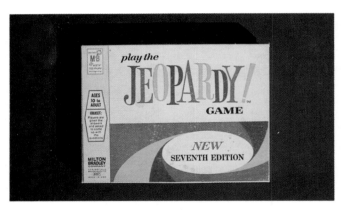

Jeopardy! Game,
1964, by Milton Bradley.
$10

Jet World Trade and Travel Game,
1975, by Milton Bradley.
$40

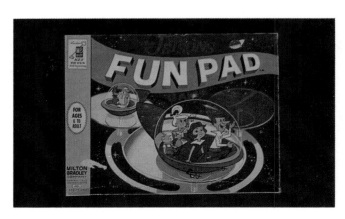

The Jetsons Fun Pad Game,
1963, by Milton Bradley.
$85

Jimmy The Greek, Odds Maker Football,
1974, by Aurora.
$15

The Joker's Wild Game,
1973, by Milton Bradley.
$10

Jumble, 1975, by Cardinal.
$10

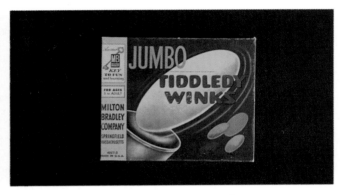

Jumbo Tiddledy Winks,
1963, by Milton Bradley.
$10

Junior Executive Game,
1955, by Whitman.
$25

J. Fred Muggs Round The World
1955, by Garbriel & Sons $90

Jackie Robinson Baseball Game
1950's, by Gotham $200

James Bond Message from M
1966, by Ideal $150

Jet Race Game
1960's, by Warren $20

Jetsons Out of This World
1962, by Transogram $125

Jetsons Rosie the Robot
1962, by Transogram $100

Jetsons Space Age Game
1962, by Transogram $100

Jim Prentice Electric Baseball
1950's, by Electric Game Co. $30

Jockette
1950's, by Jockette Co. $30

John Drake Secret Agent
1966, by Milton Bradley $65

Johnny Quest
1964, by Transogram $100

Johnny Ringo
1960, by Transogram $75

Johnny Unitas Football
1970, by Pro Mentor $50

Justice League of America
1967, by Hasbro $125

Justice
1954, by Lowell $80

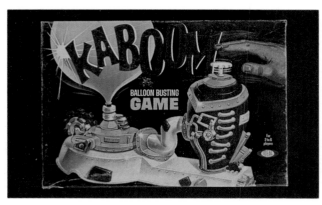

Kaboom Balloon Busting Game,
1965, by Ideal.
$20

Kennedy's, Exciting New Game of,
1962, by Transco.
$75

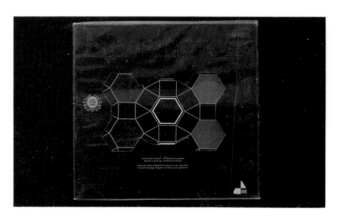

Kensington, 1979,
by Forbes Taylor.
$15

Keyword A Crossword Game,
1953, by Parker Brothers.
$15

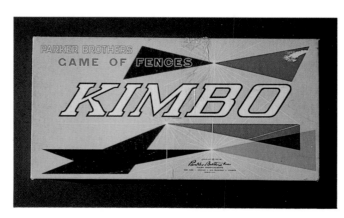

Kimbo, Game of Fences,
1960, by Parker Brothers.
$20

King Kong, 1976,
by Ideal.
$25

King Zor The Dinosaur Game,
1962, by Ideal.
$80

Kojak, The Stake Out Detective Game,
1975, by Milton Bradley.
$20

Kreskin's ESP, 1967,
by Milton Bradley.
$25

Ka-Bala
1965, by Transogram $70

Kar-Zoon
1964, by Whitman $30

Karate, The Game of
1964, by Selchow & Righter $30

Kentucky Derby
1969, by Whitman $25

King Kong
1966, by Milton Bradley $40

King Leonardo and His Subjects
1960, by Milton Bradley $35

King of the Sea
1975, by Ideal $40

King Oil
1974, by Parker Brothers $25

Know the Stars and Planets
1960, by Milton Bradley $50

Kommissar
1966, by Selchow & Righter $40

Kooky Carnival
1969, by Milton Bradley $35

Korg: 70,000 BC
1974, by Milton Bradley $25

Kukla and Ollie
1962, by Parker Brothers $50

Labyrinth Space Control,
1960's, by Cardinal.
$30

Land of the Giants,
1968, by Ideal.
$85

Las-Vegas-Wild, 1954,
by Lith-O-Ware.
$20

Let's Drive, Road Safety Fun Game,
1968, by Milton Bradley.
$15

Let's Make A Deal,
1974, by Ideal.
$20

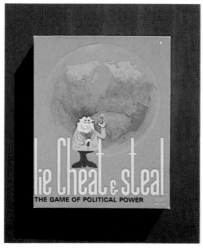

Lie Cheat & Steal, The Game of Political Power,
1971, by Dynamic Games.
$20

Limbo Legs, 1969,
by Milton Bradley.
$30

Lost in Space Game, 1965,
by Milton Bradley.
$85

The Love Computer, 1970,
by Multiple Toy Makers.
$25

Lucky Bingo, 1960's
by Transogram.
$10

Luftwaffe, The Game of
Aerial Combat over Germany 1943-45,
1971, by Avalon Hill.
$20

Lunar Landing Game, 1969,
by Lay's Packing Co.
$50

L'il Abner Game
1969, by Parker Brothers $45

Lancer
1968, by Remco $65

Land of the Lost
1975, by Milton Bradley $40

Land on the Moon
1960 . . . . $35

Laramie
1960, by Lowell $75

Lassie
1965, by Game Gems $50

Last Straw
1966, by Schaper $20

Laurel and Hardy Game
1962, by Transogram $50

Laverne & Shirley
1977, by Parker Brothers $15

LeMans
1961, by Avalon Hill $35

Leave It To Beaver Ambush
1959, by Hasbro $100

Leave It To Beaver Money Maker
1959, by Hasbro $100

**Leave It To Beaver Rocket
to the Moon**
1959, by Hasbro $100

Legend of Jesse James
1966, by Milton Bradley $80

Lie Detector
1960, by Mattel $40

Linkup
1972, by American Greetings . . . $15

Linus the Lionhearted
1965, by Transogram $75

Lippy The Lion
1962, by Transogram $60

Little Black Sambo
1952, by Cadaco $125

Little Noddy's Taxi Game
1956, by Parker Brothers $55

Little Red Schoolhouse
1952, by Parker Brothers $35

**Liz Taylor & Mystery of the
Crown Jewels**
1963, by Ideal $45

Lobby Political Game
1950's, by Milton Bradley $35

Lone Ranger & The Silver Bullets
1959, by A.A. Gaffney & Sons . . $120

Lone Ranger
1956, by Parker Brothers $50

Lone Ranger
1966, by Milton Bradley $30

Lone Ranger & Tonto Spin Game
1967, by Pressman $25

Longball
1975, by Ashburn Industries $30

Look Out Below
1968, by Ideal $35

Looney Tunes Game
1968, by Milton Bradley $50

Lost Gold
1975, by Parker Brothers $20

Lost In Space 3D Action
1966, by Remco $150

Lucille Ball Cross Up
1974, by Milton Bradley $35

Lucy Show Game
1962, by Transogram $85

Lucy's Tea Party
1971, by Milton Bradley $40

The Mad Magazine Game,
1979, by Parker Brothers.
$25

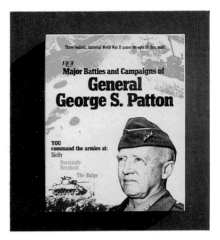

Major Battles and Campaigns of
General George S. Patton,
1974, by Research Games.
$25

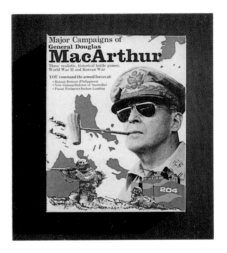

Major Campaigns of
General Douglas MacArthur,
1974, by Research Games.
$25

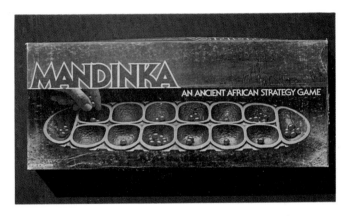

Mandinka An Ancient African Strategy Game,
1978, by Milton Bradley.
$25

The Man From U.N.C.L.E. Game,
Napoleon Solo, 1965, by Ideal.
$60

The Man From U.N.C.L.E.
Spy Magic Tricks, 1965, by Gilbert.
$125

The Man From U.N.C.L.E. The Thrush
"Ray-Gun Affair" Game,
1966, by Ideal.
$125

Manhunt, 1972,
by Milton Bradley.
$15

Margie, The Game of Whoopee!,
1961, by Milton Bradley.
$30

Master Mind 44,
1972, by Invicta.
$20

Masterpiece, The Art Auction Game,
1970, by Parker Brothers.
$25

Match Game, 1974,
by Milton Bradley.
$10

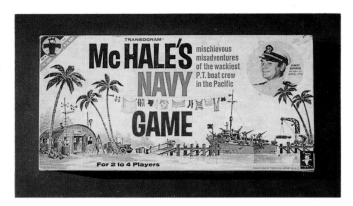

McHale's Navy Game,
1962, by Transogram.
$60

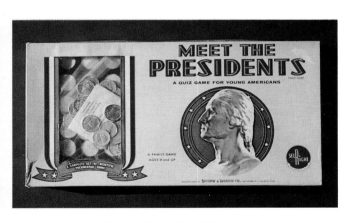

Meet The Presidents,
1961, by Selchow and Righter.
$25

Monopoly, 1964,
by Parker Brothers.
$15

The Monster Squad Game,
1977, by Milton Bradley.
$60

The Mother Goose Game,
1971, by Cadaco.
$20

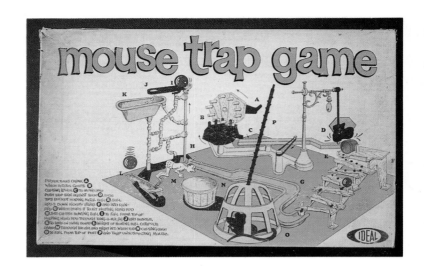

Mouse Trap Game,
1963, by Ideal.
$35

Mr. Potato Head, 1960's
by Hasbro.
$15

Mr. President, 1967,
by 3M.
$20

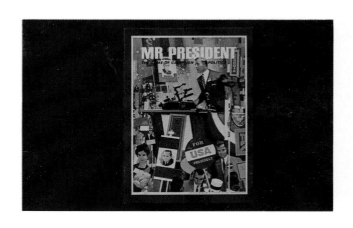

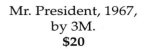

M*A*S*H
1975, by Transogram $25

Mad's Spy vs. Spy
1956, by Milton Bradley $35

Magic Midway
1962, by Cadaco $25

Magilla Gorilla
1964, by Ideal $100

Magnetic Flying Saucers
1950, by Pressman $35

Magnificent Race
1975, by Parker Brothers $25

Mail Run
1960, by Quality Games $40

Management
1960, by Avalon Hill $35

Mandrake The Magician Game
1966, by Transogram $70

Marblehead
1969, by Ideal $30

Marlin Perkins Zoo Parade
1955, by Cadaco $60

Mary Hartman, Mary Hartman
1977, by Reiss $30

Mary Poppins Carousel
1965, by Parker Brothers $15

Mary Poppins
1964, by Whitman $30

Masquerade Party
1955, by Bettye-B $55

Men Into Space
1960, by Milton Bradley $80

Mentor
1961, by Hasbro $50

Merry Milkman
1955, by Hasbro $75

Merv Griffin's Word for Word
1963, by Mattel $25

Mickey Mouse Club in Disneyland
1955, by Whitman $75

Mickey Mouse Game Box
1953, by Parker Brothers $75

Mighty Hercules Game
1963, by Hasbro $125

Mighty Mouse Rescue Game
1956, by H.G. Toys $45

Milton the Monster
1966, by Milton Bradley $45

Mind Over Matter
1968, by Transogram $20

Miss America Pageant Game
1974, by Parker Brothers $25

Miss Popularity
1961, by Transogram $30

Missing Links
1964, by Milton Bradley $20

Mission Impossible
1966, by Ideal $80

Mod Squad
1968, by Remco $85

Monkees Game
1967, by Transogram $75

Monkeys and Coconuts
1965, by Schaper $35

Mork & Mindy
1978, by Parker Brothers $25

Movie Moguls
1970, by Research Games $25

Mr. Ed
1962, by Parker Brothers $75

Mr. Machine Game
1961, by Ideal $75

Mr. Magoo Visits the Zoo
1961, by Lowell $35

Mr. Novak
1963, by Transogram $45

Mr. Ree Detective Game
1957, by Selchow & Righter $50

Munsters Drag Race Game
1964, by Hasbro $125

Munsters Masquerade Party Game
1964, by Hasbro $125

Munsters Picnic Game
1965, by Hasbro $125

Muppet Show
1977, by Parker Brothers $25

Murder on the Orient Express
1967, by Ideal $35

Mushmouse and Punkin Puss
1964, by Ideal $55

My Fair Lady
1962, by Standard Toycraft $40

My Favorite Martian
1963, by Transogram $85

Mystery Date
1965, by Milton Bradley $40

Mystic Skull
1964, by Ideal $40

The Newlywed Game, 1960's,
by Hasbro.
$20

The New Price Is Right Game,
1973, by Milton Bradley.
$15

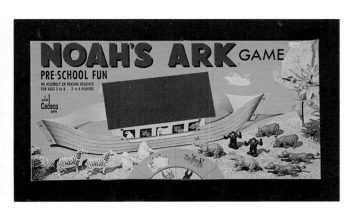

Noah's Ark Game, 1971,
by Cadaco.
$20

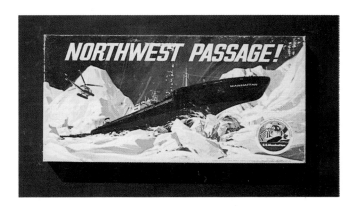

Northwest Passage!,
1969, by Impact Communication.
$25

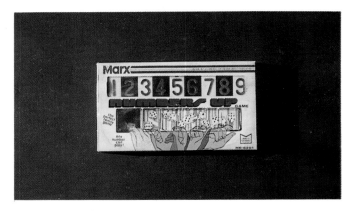

Numbers Up Game,
1974, by Marx.
$15

Name That Tune Game
1959, by Milton Bradley $25

Nancy Drew Mystery Game
1957, by Parker Brothers $40

National Velvet
1961, by Transogram $35

Navy Log TV Game
1957, by Lowell Toy Mfg. Co. . . . $70

Nearsighted Mr. Magoo
1970, by Transogram $40

New Adventures of Gilligan Game
1974, by Milton Bradley $40

New York World's Fair
1964, by Milton Bradley $60

Nieuchess
1961, by Avalon Hill $20

Nile
1967, by E.S. Lowe $20

No Time for Sergeants Games
1964, by Ideal $45

Nuclear War
1965, by Douglas Malewicki $40

Number Please
1961, by Parker Brothers $20

Numble
1968, by Selchow & Righter $25

Nurse's Game
1963, by Ideal $30

Oh Hell, 1973,
by Cadaco.
$25

Oh No, 1967,
by Milton Bradley.
$20

Operation, 1965,
by Milton Bradley.
$20

Orbit, 1959,
by Parker Brothers.
$85

The Original Clubhouse Bingo, Our Gang,
1958, by Gabriel & Sons Co.
$75

Oswald Jacoby Backgammon,
1973, by Pressman.
$10

The Outer Limits,
1964, by Milton Bradley.
$150

Octopus
1954, by Norton Games $50

Octrix
1970, by 3M $20

Official Boston Marathon Game
1978, by Perl Products $15

Official Globetrotter Basketball
1950's, by Meljak $60

Official Hopalong Cassidy Lasso Game
1950, by Transogram $100

Organized Crime
1974, by Koplow $25

Origins of World War II
1971, by Avalon Hill $20

Outdoor Survival
1972, by Avalon Hill $20

Outlaws
1961, by Transogram $100

Overland Trail
1964, by Transogram $100

Panzer Blitz, 1970,
by Avalon Hill.
$15

Parcheesi, A Royal Game of India,
1950's, by Selchow and Righter.
$15

Park and Shop, The Shopping Game,
1960, by Milton Bradley.
$40

The Partridge Family Game,
1971, by Milton Bradley.
$20

Pass-Out, 1971,
by Pass Out Games.
$20

Password, 1962,
by Milton Bradley.
$15

Pathfinder, 1977,
by Milton Bradley.
$20

Patty Duke Game,
1963, by Milton Bradley.
$30

Pay Day, 1975,
by Parker Brothers.
$15

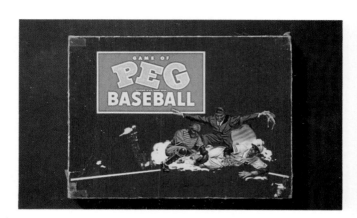

Peg Baseball, Game of,
1954, by Parker Brothers.
$40

Perquackey, 1956,
by Shreve.
$15

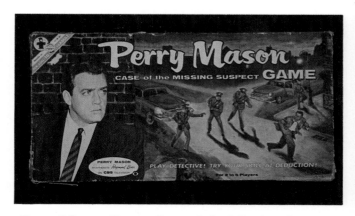

Perry Mason Game, Case of the Missing Suspect,
1959, by Transogram.
$45

Phlounder, 1962,
by 3M.
$20

Pink Panther Game,
1977, by Warren.
$60

Pit, The World's Liveliest Trading Game,
1964, by Parker Brothers.
$20

Planet of the Apes, 1974,
by Milton Bradley.
$25

Play Your Hunch, TV's Popular Guessing Game,
1960, by Transogram.
$30

Point of Law, 1972,
by 3M.
$25

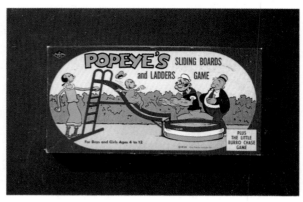

Popeye's Sliding Boards and Ladders Game,
1958, by Built-Rite.
$75

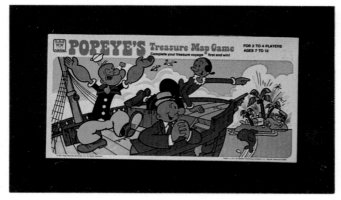

Popeye's Treasure Map Game,
1977, by Whitman.
$40

Post Office Game,
1968, by Hasbro.
$30

Pro Draft, Team Building Football Game,
1974, by Parker Brothers.
$20

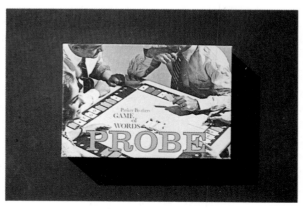

Probe, Game of Words,
1964, by Parker Brothers.
$15

Professor Wonderful's Wonder-Lab,
1964, by Gilbert.
$45

Pull The Rug Out Game,
1968, by Schaper.
$35

Punch Line, 1978,
by Parker Brothers.
$20

Put and Take, 1956,
by Schaper.
$25

Par '73
1961, by Big Top Games $20

Par Golf
1950's, by National Games Inc. . . $45

Park & Shop
1952, by Traffic Game Co. $75

Pass It On
1978, by Selchow & Righter $15

Pax
1955, by Chesapeake Bay
Trading Co. $50

Peanuts
1959, by Selchow & Righter $50

Pebbles Flintstone
1962, by Transogram $50

Person-Alysis
1957, by Lowell Toy Mfg. Co. . . . $30

Peter Gunn Detective Game
1960, by Lowell Toys $70

Peter Pan
1953, by Transogram $60

Peter Potamus
1964, by Ideal $125

Pettycoat Junction
1963, by Toycraft $60

Phalanx
1964, by Whitman $40

Phantom of the Opera Mystery Game
1963, by Hasbro $150

Phantom Game
1966, by Transogram $125

Phil Silvers You'll Never Get Rich
1955, by Gardner $65

Philip Marlow Game
1960, by Transogram $50

Pinky Lee and the Runaway Frankfurters
1954, by Whiting $75

Pinky Lee Who Am I
1954 . . . . $75

Pitchin Pal
1952, by Cadaco $30

Playdirt!
1973, by Sports Illustrated $15

Ploy
1970, by 3M $15

Poison Ivy Game
1969, by Ideal $25

Poka-Tile
1961, by Ideal $20

Police Patrol Action Game
1950's, by Hasbro $60

Policeman
1957, by Selchow & Righter $35

Pop Ye Top
1968, by Milton Bradley $35

Price is Right
1962, by Lowell $25

Prince Valiant
1955, by Transogram $45

Pro Football
1964, by Milton Bradley $20

Prospecting
1957, by Selchow & Righter $50

Psych-Out
1971, by Milton Bradley. $15

Pursuit!
1973, by Aurora $20

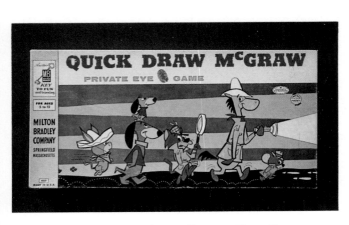

Quick Draw McGraw, Private Eye Game,
1960, by Milton Bradley.
$85

Quinto,
1964, by 3M.
$20

Quick Draw McGraw Moving Target
1960, by Knickerbocker Plastic $85

Racko, 1961,
by Milton Bradley.
$15

Radar Search Game, Electronic,
1969, by Ideal.
$45

Raggedy Ann Game,
1954, by Milton Bradley.
$45

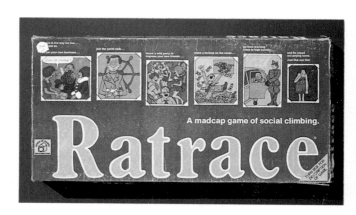

Ratrace, 1970,
by House of Games - Waddingtons.
$20

The Rat Patrol Desert Combat Game,
1966, by Transogram.
$75

Recall, Game of Observation,
1968, by Milton Bradley.
$30

The Red Rover Game,
1963, by Cadaco-Ellis.
$30

The Restless Gun Game,
1959, by Milton Bradley.
$55

Revlon's $64,000 Question,
1955, by Lowell Toy Mfg.
$60

Rich Uncle The Stock Market Game,
1955, by Parker Brothers.
$35

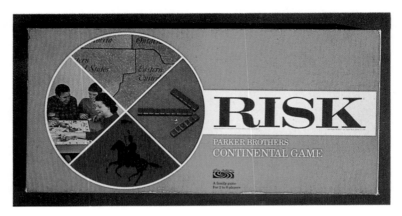

Risk, 1968,
by Parker Brothers.
$20

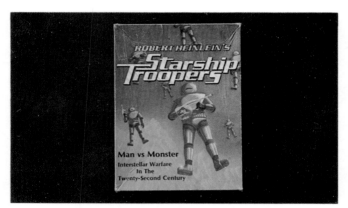

Robert Heinlein's Starship Troopers,
Man vs Monster, 1976,
by Avalon Hill.
$40

The Robert Q. Lewis Family Game Chest,
1956, by National Games.
$20

Rollacolor Family Game,1965,
by Rich-Mar Sco-Dar Inc.
$20

Rowan & Martins Laugh-in,
Squeeze Your Bippy Game, 1968,
by Hasbro.
$70

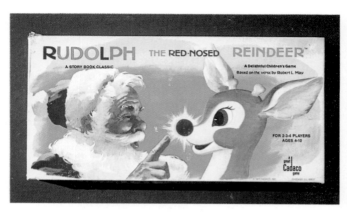

Rudolph The Red Nosed Reindeer,
1977, by Cadaco.
$20

Ruff and Reddy Spills and Thrills of the Circus
Game, Hanna-Barbera, 1962,
by Transogram.
$60

Rummy Royal, A Family Game,
1965, by Whitman.
$15

Russian Roulette, 1975,
by Selchow and Righter.
$15

R.S.V.P.
1966, by Selchow & Righter $15

Raceway
1950's, by B & B Toy Mfg. Co. . . $30

Rail Baron
1977, by Avalon Hill $15

Ramar of the Jungle
1953, by Dexter Wayne $65

Rat Patrol Spin Game
1967, by Pressman $60

Rawhide
1960, by Lowell $80

Razzle Dazzle Football Game
1954, by Texantics Unlimited . . . $35

Rebel
1961, by Ideal $75

Regatta
1966, by 3M $20

Rib-Bit
1974, by Genesis Enterprises $15

Rich Farmer, Poor Farmer
1978, by McJay Game Co. $15

Ricochet Rabbit
1965, by Ideal $100

Rifleman
1959, by Milton Bradley $75

Rin-Tin-Tin
1955, by Transogram $70

Ripcord
1962, by Lowell $50

Road Runner
1968, by Milton Bradley $60

Robin Hood
1973, by Parker Brothers $25

Robot Sam The Answer Man
1950, by Jacmar $40

Rocket Patrol Magnetic Target Game
1950's, by SH Japan $60

Rocket Race to Saturn
1950, by Lido Toy $35

Rocket Satellite Action Game
1950's, by Traco $85

Rocky & His Friends
1960, by Milton Bradley $50

Roger Maris Action Baseball
1962, by Pressman $40

Roger Staubach ABC Monday Night Football
1973, by Aurora $30

Roman X, The Game of Caesars
1964, by Selchow & Righter $25

Route 66
1960, by Transogram $125

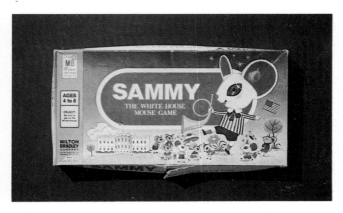

Sammy, The White House Mouse Game,
1977, by Milton Bradley.
$20

Score Four, 1975,
by Lakeside.
$15

Scrabble, 1953,
by Selchow and Righter.
$15

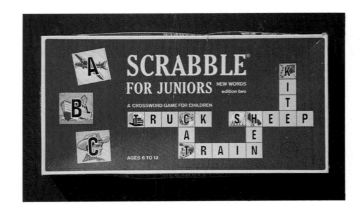

Scrabble for Juniors, 1964,
by Selchow and Righter Co.
$15

Sealab 2020 Game, 1973,
by Milton Bradley.
$30

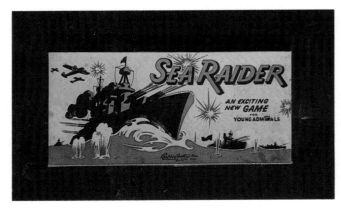

Sea Raider, 1963,
by Parker Brothers.
$30

Sentence Cube Game - Scrabble,
1971, by Selchow and Righter.
$10

Seven Seas The Game of Trade,
1960, by Cadaco-Ellis.
$45

Singing Numbers Game,
1960, by Parker Brothers.
$20

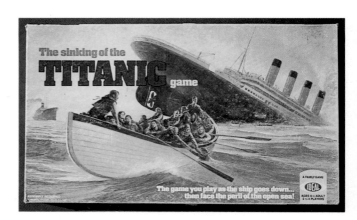

The Sinking of the Titanic Game,
1976, by Ideal.
$20

Situation 4, 1968,
by Parker Brothers.
$20

The Six Million Dollar Man,
1975, by Parker Brothers.
$20

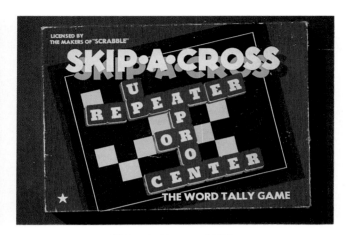

Skip-A-Cross, 1953,
by Cadaco-Ellis.
$15

Skipper Game, Barbies Little Sister,
1964, by Mattel.
$30

Skittle Baseball, 1971, by Aurora.
$30

Snoopy and the Red Baron,
1970, by Milton Bradley.
$25

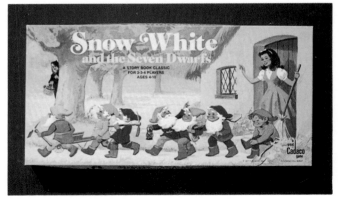

Snow White and the Seven Dwarfs,
1977, by Cadaco.
$25

Sorry! 1958,
by Parker Brothers.
$20

Space Pilot, 1951,
by Cadaco-Ellis.
$65

Spare-Time Bowling, 1974,
by Lakeside.
$10

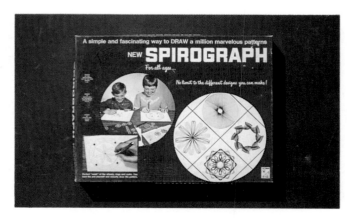

Spirograph, 1967,
by Kenner.
$15

Squander, 1965,
by Avalon Hill.
$20

Square Mile, 1962,
by Milton Bradley.
$20

Square Off, 1972,
by Parker Brothers.
$15

Squares, 1950's,
by Schraper.
$15

Stadium Checkers, 1952,
by Schaper.
$15

Starsky and Hutch, Detective Game,
1977, by Milton Bradley.
$15

Star Trek Game, 1967,
by Ideal.
$125

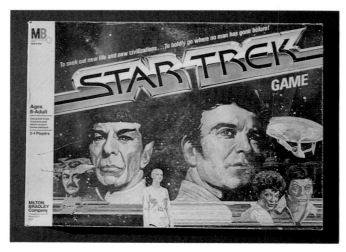

Star Trek Game, 1979,
by Milton Bradley.
$40

Stay Alive, 1978,
by Milton Bradley.
$15

Stock Market Game, 1963,
by Whitman.
$15

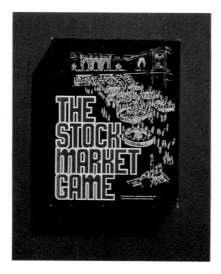

The Stock Market Game, 1970,
by Avalon Hill.
$15

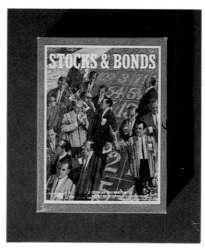

Stocks & Bonds, 1964,
by 3M.
$15

Stratego Game, 1970,
by Milton Bradley.
$20

Strategy Poker, 1968,
by Milton Bradley.
$15

Sudden Death, 1978,
by Gabriel.
$25

Summit, 1961,
by Milton Bradley.
$45

Calling Superman,
1954, by Transogram.
$100

Super Spy, 1971,
by Milton Bradley.
$25

Sure Shot Baseball Game,
1970, by Ideal.
$25

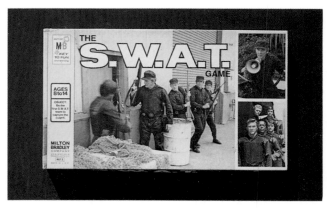

The S.W.A.T. Game,
1976, by Milton Bradley.
$20

Swahili Game, 1968,
by Milton Bradley.
$20

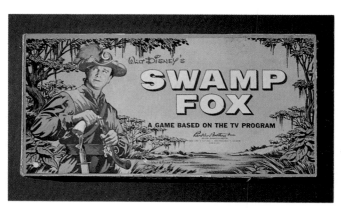

Swamp Fox, Walt Disney's,
1960, by Parker Brothers.
$60

"Swayze", 1954,
by Milton Bradley.
$35

Sweeps, The Popular "Money" Game,
1950's, by E.E. Fairchild Corp.
$20

Swivel, 1972,
by Milton Bradley.
$20

Safari
1950, by Selchow & Righter $50

Sale of the Century
1970, by Milton Bradley $15

Salvo, The Game of Naval Strategy
1961, by Ideal $50

Samsonite Basketball
1969, by Samsonite $15

Say When!
1961, by Parker Brothers $20

Scan
1970, by Parker Brothers $15

Scramble, Air Battle Game
1970's, by Victory $20

Screwball, The Mad Mad Game
1958, by Transogram $70

Sea Hunt
1961, by Lowell $60

Sergeant Preston Game
1956, by Milton Bradley $50

Seven Keys
1961, by Ideal $20

Shae-Ee: The Game of Destiny
1963, by Ideal $30

Shari Lewis in Shariland
1959, by Transogram $50

Shenanigans Game
1964, by Milton Bradley $40

Sheriff of Dodge City
1966, by Parker Brothers $30

Sherlock Holmes, The Game of the Great Detective
1956, by National Games $60

Shindig
1965, by Remco $75

Shotgun Slade Game
1960, by Milton Bradley $50

Show-Biz, The Game of the Stars
1956, by Lowell $50

Siege
1966, by Milton Bradley $30

Sigmund and the Sea Monsters Game
1974, by Milton Bradley $25

Silly Sidney the Elephant
1963, by Transogram $75

Sinbad
1978, by Cadaco $40

Sir Lancelot
1957, by Whiting $35

Skatterbug
1951, by Parker Brothers $45

Skunk
1953, by Shaper $30

Sky Lanes
1958, by Parker Brothers $90

Sky's The Limit
1955, by Kohner Brothers $35

Sly,
1975, by Amway $15

Smack-A-Roo Game
1964, by Mattel $50

Smokey The Bear
1961, by Ideal $55

Snafu
1952, by Haswell $15

Snake Eyes
1957, by Selchow & Righter $50

Snake's Alive
1966, by Ideal $20

Snapshot
1972, by Parker Brothers $15

Snoopy Come Home
1966, by Milton Bradley $35

Snoopy
1960, by Selchow & Righter $50

Solar Conquest
1966, by A-Tech $35

Son of Hercules Game
1966, by Milton Bradley $40

Sonar Sub Hunt
1961, by Mattel $40

Soupy Sales
1960, by Milton Bradley $60

Source of the Nile
1979, by Avalon Hill $20

Space Angel
1965, by Transogram $60

Space Chase
1967, by United
    Nations Constructors $45

Space Game
1953, by Parker Brothers $65

Space Hop
1973, by Teaching Concepts $30

Space Race
1969, by Ed-U-Cards $20

Space 1999
1976, by Milton Bradley $25

Speed Buggy Game
1973, by Milton Bradley $25

Speed Circuit
1971, by 3M $25

Speedway, Big Bopper Game
1961, by Ideal $35

**Spiro T. Agnew American History
Challenge Game**
1971, by Gabriel $50

Spy Detective Game
1960, by Mattel $20

Squad Car
1950's, by National Games Inc . . $50

Squander
1965, by Avalon Hill $20

Stage Coach
1955, by Schaper $60

Stagecoach West
1961, by Transogram $75

Stampede
1956, by Gabriel $30

Star Reporter
1954, by Parker Brothers $70

Star Trek Game
1974, by Hasbro $50

**Star Wars Game, Escape from
Death Star**
1977, by Kenner $20

Star Wars Destroy Death Game
1977, by Kenner $20

Starship Troopers
1976, by Avalon Hill $20

States & Statesman
1959, by Reingell Industries $30

Steve Canyon Air Force Game
1959, by Lowell $85

Steve Scott, Space Scout
1952, by Transogram $70

Sting Game
1976, by Ideal $25

Stingray-The Underwater Game
1966, by Transogram $100

Stock Car Racing Game
1956, by Whitman $40

Stoney Burke
1963, by Transogram $50

Straight Arrow
1950, by Selchow & Righter $75

Straightaway
1961, by Selchow & Righter $50

Strategic Command
1950, by Transogram $50

Strike It Rich
1956, by Lowell $40

Student Survival Game
1968, by Game Masters $25

Stump the Stars
1962, by Ideal $35

Stump
1968, by Milton Bradley $20

Sub Attack Game
1965, by Milton Bradley $30

Sub Search
1973, by Milton Bradley $25

Super Market
1953, by Selchow & Righter $40

Superboy
1965, by Hasbro $100

Supercar Road Race
1962, by Toycraft $60

Superman and Superboy
1967, by Milton Bradley $100

Superman Match II
1979, by Ideal $35

Superman Spin Game
1967, by Pressman $60

Supermarket Sweep
1966, by Milton Bradley $35

Superstar Baseball
1966, by Sports Illustrated $20

Superstition
1977, by Milton Bradley $20

Sure Shot Hockey
1970, by Ideal $20

Surfside 6
1962, by Lowell $85

Surprise Package
1961, by Ideal $35

Swack
1968, by Ideal $20

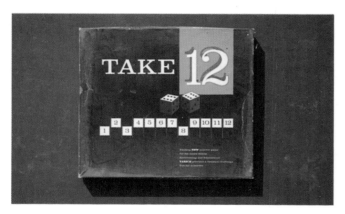

Take 12, 1959,
by Phillips Publishers.
$20

Tank Battle Game, 1975,
by Milton Bradley.
$30

Tally Ho!, 1961,
by Whitman.
$20

Tell It to the Judge,
1959, by Parker Brothers.
$50

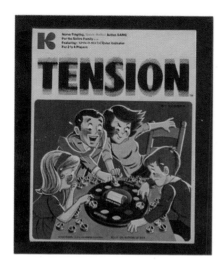

Tension, 1960's
by Kohner Brothers.
$20

Terrytoons, Hide n'Seek Game,
1960, by Transogram.
$50

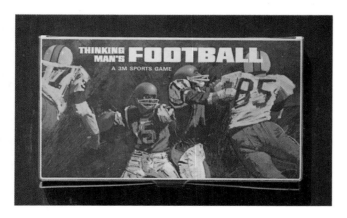

Thinking Man's Football,
1969, by 3M.
$20

Third Man, 1969,
by Saalfield.
$25

Three On A Match Game,
1972, by Milton Bradley.
$15

Thrift, 1963,
by American Publishing Corp.
$15

Tic-Tac Dough TV Quiz Game,
1957, by Transogram.
$20

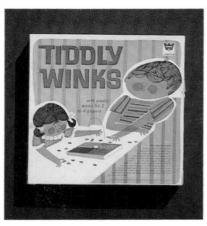

Tiddly Winks, 1966,
by Whitman.
$10

The Time Tunnel Game,
1966, by Ideal.
$125

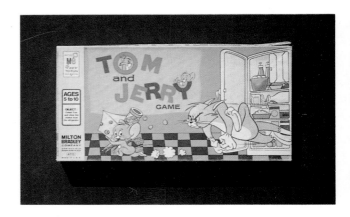

Tom and Jerry Game,
1977, by Milton Bradley.
$30

Traffic, A Game of Real Driving Experiences,
Buy! Sell! Trade! Win a Cadillac!,
1968, by E. S. Lowe.
$30

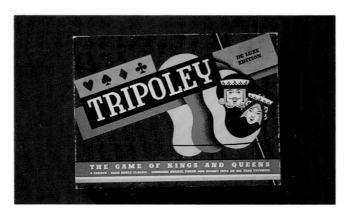

Tripoley De Luxe Edition,
1955, by Cadaco-Ellis.
$15

Tripoley Junior, 1962,
by Cadaco-Ellis.
$15

Trouble, 1965,
by Kohner.
$20

TV Jackpot Game,
1975, by Milton Bradley.
$15

Tweety and Sylvester's
"I Tawt I Taw A Puddy Tat" Game,
1972, by Whitman.
$25

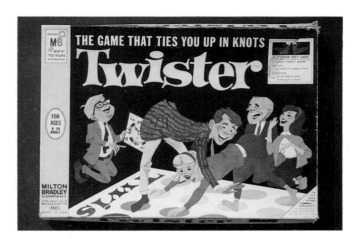

Twister, 1966,
by Milton Bradley.
$25

Twixt, 1962,
by 3M.
$20

Tales of Texas Rangers
1956, by All-Fair $60

Tales of Wells Fargo Game
1959, by Milton Bradley $75

Talking Football
1971, by Mattel $15

Tammy Game
1963, by Ideal $35

Tarzan to the Rescue
1977, by Milton Bradley $25

Tee Off by Sam Snead
1973, by Glenn Industries $40

Terrytoons Mighty Mouse Game
1978, by Milton Bradley $35

They're At The Post
1976, MAAS Marketing $25

They're Off
1952, by Parker Brothers $70

Thing Ding
1966, by Schaper $75

Thirteen
1959, by Cadaco $20

This Is Your Life
1954, by Lowell $45

Thistle
1966, by Parker Brothers $20

Three Musketeers
1958, by Milton Bradley $50

Three Stooges Fun House
1959, by Lowell $125

Thunderball, James Bond 007
1965, by Milton Bradley $25

Thunderbirds
1967, by Parker Brothers $75

Ticker Tape
1963, by Cadaco $65

Tiny Tim – Beautiful Things
1970, by Parker Brothers $50

Tip-it
1965, by Ideal $20

Tom Swift Game
1966, by Parker Brothers $35

Tomorrowland: Rocket to the Moon
1956, by Parker Brothers $75

Tootsie Roll Train Game
1969, by Hasbro $25

Top Cat
1962, by Whitman $75

Top Cop
1961, by Cadaco $60

Top Scholar
1957, by Cadaco $35

Top Secret
1956, by National Games $75

Touche Turtle
1964, by Ideal $125

Touring
1950's, by Parker Brothers $15

Track Meet
1972, by Sports Illustrated $20

Trade Winds
1960, by Parker Brothers $40

Traffic Jam
1954, by Harett-Gilmar $60

Trail Blazers
1964, by Milton Bradley $60

Trap-Em!
1957, by Selchow & Righter $25

Travel America
1950, by Jacmar $35

Treffles
1976, by Games and Names $15

Tru-Action Electric Basketball
1961, by Tudor $30

Truth or Consequences
1955, by Gabriel $35

Tudor Electric Horse Racing Game
1959, by Tudor $40

Tudor Electric Sports Car Race
1959, by Tudor $40

Tumble Bumble
1970, by Ideal $20

Twelve o'Clock High
1965, by Ideal $65

Twenty-One TV Quiz Game
1950's, by Lowell $50

Twiggy
1967, by Milton Bradley $60

Twilight Zone
1964, by Ideal $175

Twinkles Game
1961, by Milton Bradley $100

Uncle Wiggily Game,
1954, by Milton Bradley.
$35

The Ungame, Tell It Like It Is . . . With,
1975, by The Ungame Co.
$25

Vegas, 1969,
by Hasbro.
$20

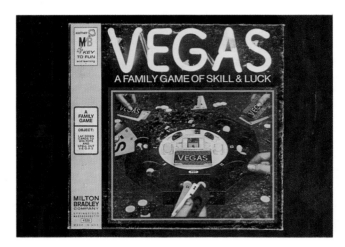

Vegas, 1973,
by Milton Bradley.
$20

Video Village, 1960,
by Milton Bradley.
$35

Voyage To The Bottom Of The Sea Game,
1964, by Milton Bradley.
$60

Undercover: Game of Secret Agents
1960, by Cadaco $50

Underdog
1964, by Milton Bradley $60

**Undersea World of
Jacques Cousteau**
1968, by Parker Brothers $40

Varsity
1955, by Cadaco-Ellis $20

Viet Nam
1965, by Gamescience $100

Vince Lombardi's Game
1970, by Research Games $40

Virginian
1962, by Transogram $75

Waddington's Spy Ring, 1965,
by John Waddington Ltd.
$30

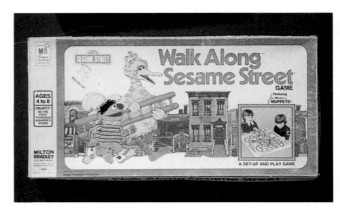

Walk Along Sesame Street Game,
1975, by Milton Bradley.
$20

Walt Disney's Peter Pan A Game of Adventure,
1953, by Transogram.
$40

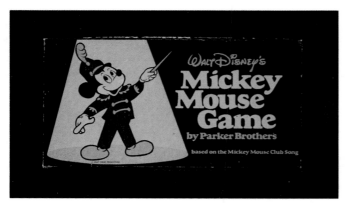

Walt Disney's Mickey Mouse Game,
1976, by Parker Brothers.
$30

Walt Disney's Frontierland Game,
1955, by Parker Brothers.
$40

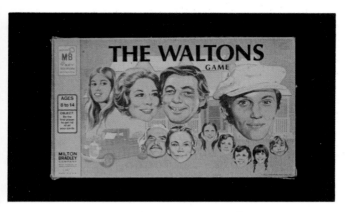

The Waltons Game, 1974,
by Milton Bradley.
$20

Watch Word, 1966,
by Ideal.
$30

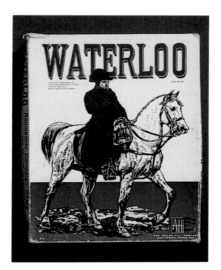

Waterloo, 1962,
by Avalon Hill.
$50

Welcome Back, Kotter,
1976, by Ideal.
$15

Wide World Travel Game,
1957, by Parker Brothers.
$35

Wild Bill Hickoks, The Cavalry and
The Indians Game,
1956, by Built-Rite.
$85

Wing-It, 1971,
by Schaper.
$30

Winner Spinner, 1958,
by Whitman.
$20

Win, Place and Show, 1977,
by Avalon Hill.
$15

The Wizard of Oz Game,
1974, by Cadaco.
$20

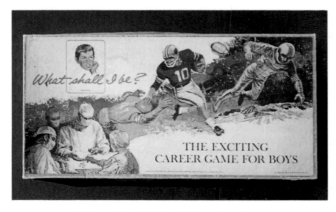

What Shall I Be? The Exciting
Career Game For Boys, 1968,
by Selchow & Righter.
$20

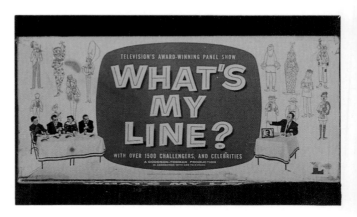

What's My Line?, 1955,
by Lowell.
$50

Whosit?, 1976,
by Parker Brothers.
$15

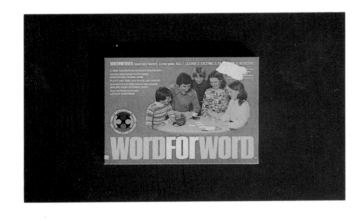

Word for Word, 1975,
by Edu-Cards.
$10

World's Fair Game, the Official New York,
1963, by Milton Bradley.
$25

W.C. Fields
1972, by Gamekeepers $25

Wagon Train
1964, by Milton Bradley $65

Wally Gator
1962, by Transogram $65

Wanted: Dead or Alive
1959, by Lowell $100

War of the Networks
1979, by Hasbro $40

Water Pollution Game
1970, by Urban Systems $30

Watergate Scandal
1973, by American Sym. Corp. . . $20

Waterworks
1972, by Parker Brothers $20

Weird-ohs Game
1964, by Ideal $100

Welfare
1978, by Jedco $25

Wells Fargo
1961, by Milton Bradley $60

Wendy the Good Little Witch
1966, by Milton Bradley $75

West Point Story
1961, by Transogram $35

What's Up Doc?
1970, by Whitman $25

Who Am I? No. 1
1970, by Zundervan $20

Who Can Beat Nixon?
1970, by Dynamic Design $25

Who? Game of Hidden Identity
1951, by Parker Brothers $35

Whodunit
1972, by Selchow & Righter $20

Wild Life
1971, by Lowe $35

Wild Wild West
1966, by Transogram $80

Window Shopping
1962, by Lowell $35

Winnie The Pooh
1964, by Parker Brothers $35

Witch Pitch
1970, by Parker Brothers $25

Wizard of Oz
1962, by Lowell $35

Wolfman Game
1963, by Hasbro $150

Wonder Woman Game
1978, by Hasbro $30

Woody Woodpecker
1956, by Cadaco $60

Wow: Pillow Fight Game
1964, by Milton Bradley $40

Wyatt Earp
1958, by Transogram $85

Yahtzee, 1956,
by E.S. Lowe.
$15

Yogi Bear Game, 1971,
by Milton Bradley.
$35

Yogie Bear Presents, Snagglepuss,
1961, by Transogram.
$80

Zap!, 1960's,
by Skor-Mor.
$20

Yacht Race
1961, by Parker Brothers $90

Yesteryear
1973, by Skor-Mor $15

Yogi Bear Go Fly A Kite
1961, by Transogram $50

You Don't Say
1963, by Milton Bradley $15

Your First Impression
1962, by Lowell $25

Yours For A Song
1962, by Lowell $40

**Zany Zoo Adventures of
Tennessee Tuxedo**
1963, by Transogram $125

Zingo
1950's, by Empire $25

Zip Code Game
1964, by Lowe $50

Zit-Zingo The Travel Game
1954, by J & J Co. $15

Zorro
1966, by Parker Brothers $90

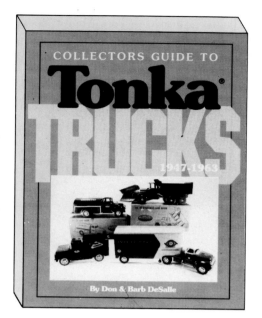

COLLECTORS GUIDE TO
Tonka®
TRUCKS

By Don & Barb DeSalle
Published by L-W Book Sales

This book includes: A complete history of the Tonka® origination; How to identify the different years of trucks; A listing of Tonka® Trucks; Sets and accessories from 1947 to 1963.

There are trucks of all types pictured such as, Cabover Trucks, Box Vans, Fire Trucks, Pickup Trucks, Tanker Trucks, and many different types of Trucks.

Send a Check or Money Order to:

L-W Book Sales
P.O. Box 69 • Gas City, IN 46933

Or Call:

1-800-777-6450

for **Visa** or **Mastercard** and **C.O.D.** order only

ORDER #1062
8 1/2" x 11" paperback – 128 pages
$19.95 + $2.00 shipping
(order 6 books to get the wholesale price of $11.97 each + $4.00 shipping)

Occupied Japan Toys

By David C. Gould & Donna Crevar-Donaldson
Published by L-W Book Sales

These toys were made between the years of 1945 to 1952 when the United States occupation of Japan took place. The toys then were exported to America. Some items were marked MIOJ and generally those marked have a higher value.

This book includes: dolls; wind-up toys; whistles; squirt guns; and many other novelties. Most are made of tin or celluloid. These toys have become very popular to collect in recent years.

Send a Check or Money Order to:

L-W Book Sales
P.O. Box 69 • Gas City, IN 46933

Or Call:

1-800-777-6450

for **Visa** or **Mastercard** and **C.O.D.** order only

ORDER #1057
8 1/2" x 11" paperback – 95 pages
$14.95 + $2.00 shipping
(order 6 books to get the wholesale price of $8.97 each + $4.00 shipping)